Josh and Jaz have three mums

Illustrations by
Amanda Wood

Hedi Argent

Published by
British Association for Adoption & Fostering
(BAAF)
Saffron House
6–10 Kirby Street
London EC1N 8TS
www.baaf.org.uk

Charity registration 275689
© Text, Hedi Argent, 2007
© Illustrations, Amanda Wood, 2007

British Library Cataloguing in Publication Data
A catalogue record for this book is available from
the British Library
ISBN 978 1 905664 12 2

Project management by Miranda Davies, BAAF
Designed and typeset by Andrew Haig & Associates
Printed in Great Britain by the Lavenham Press
Trade distribution by Turnaround Publisher
Services, Unit 3, Olympia Trading Estate, Coburg
Road, London N22 6TZ

Jaz and Josh
our family Tree

Acknowledgements
My gratitude goes to all the children, parents
and colleagues who have read and discussed
drafts of this story and made helpful
comments. I am indebted to Shaila Shah and
Miranda Davies for their support,
encouragement and attention to detail in
producing this book, and to Amanda Wood for
her lovely illustrations. I give my special
thanks to Rosie Coleman for introducing me
to "chickenspots".

About the author
Hedi Argent is an independent family
placement consultant, trainer and freelance
writer. She is the author of numerous books,
practice guides and children's booklets for
BAAF.

About the illustrator
Amanda Wood has been producing
illustrations for children for 20 years. She is
currently working towards an exhibition of her
work in France.

'Hurry up or you'll be late for school,' called Mummy Sue on Monday morning. It was Mummy Sue's turn to take Josh and Jaz to school.

Lots of their friends at school had chickenpox. On the way to school Jaz asked, 'Will I catch chickenspots?' She always called it chickenspots instead of chickenpox.

'If you catch it, I'll catch it too,' said Josh.

Their teacher, Mr Shah, said that chickenpox is very catching and that you get itchy spots all over. That's why Jaz called it chickenspots. Jaz and Josh kept looking for spots but they couldn't find any.

1

Josh and Jaz are twins. They are five years old. Their names are really Joshua and Jasmine but they like to be called Josh and Jaz.

Josh and Jaz are adopted. Being adopted means belonging to a new family when you can't live with the family you were born into.

Josh and Jaz have two mums and a puppy called Bumps. She is called Bumps because when she was very tiny she was always bumping into things.

Josh and Jaz call their two mums 'Mummy Sue' and 'Mummy Fran' for most of the time. But sometimes they just call them 'Sue' and 'Fran'.

There are many more people in the family: two grandmas, one grandpa, three aunts, four uncles and seven cousins. Josh and Jaz are part of a big family.

Josh and Jaz go to Oak Tree School. They are in Year One. They like their teacher, Mr Shah, because he has good ideas.

One week, Mr Shah and the children made a huge map showing the school and all the streets where they lived. They put the map up on the wall. Then all the children could see how they got to school. They could see how near or far they lived from each other.

That morning, Mr Shah said, 'Tomorrow we are going to make a family tree.'

They were each going to draw a tree. All the people in their families would be the leaves on the branches. The teacher explained that some children have two families.

'You may have a mum and dad who live in different homes.'

'You may have a stepmum, or stepdad, or you may be adopted.'

He wanted the children to put all their family on the tree.

And he told them not to forget their grannies and grandpas and aunties and uncles and cousins and sisters and brothers.

Then the teacher drew his own family tree to show the children how to do it.

Josh and Jaz were very quiet when Mummy Sue collected them from school. They aren't usually quiet; they usually run around the playground with their friends and make a lot of noise.

'What's the matter?' asked Sue.

Josh and Jaz didn't say anything. They shrugged their shoulders. They looked a bit upset.

When they got home, they didn't want any tea, not even a slice of gooey chocolate cake, and Sue was afraid they were coming down with chickenpox.

Josh and Jaz were beginning to look really miserable. Even Bumps couldn't cheer them up when she jumped on their laps, and tried to lick their faces, which she was not allowed to do.

Mummy Sue and Mummy Fran
live together. They take it in turn
to go to work and to stay at home.

Today Fran had been to work.
When she came home she was
surprised that the twins didn't
rush up to hug her.

Fran knew some really fun games
that no one else could play, like
"Hunt the Giant" and "Race to
the Moon". But today, Josh and Jaz
didn't want to play.

'What's the matter, aren't you
feeling well?' asked Fran.

Josh and Jaz didn't say
anything. They just
shrugged their shoulders.

'They may be coming
down with chickenpox,'
said Sue.

Then Jaz started to cry.
'I've got a tummy ache.'

Josh said he didn't want to go
to school tomorrow.

Sue and Fran took the twins on their laps and they had a cuddle.

Josh was crying as well now.

Fran asked them gently, 'Has anything happened at school to upset you?'

Josh didn't know how to say it and went on crying. Jaz cried harder and tried to speak at the same time. No one could understand what she said.

When she managed to stop crying, she said it again: 'I don't want to make a family tree. Everyone else has got a mum and a dad and we've got two mums instead.'

Mummy Sue and Mummy Fran looked serious.

Sue said, 'Let's make some tea. Then we can sit down together and sort this out. Who wants egg on toast with crispy bacon?'

Everyone wanted egg on toast with crispy bacon because it was the family favourite. The grown-ups did the cooking. The twins were in charge of making toast and buttering it. They were feeling better already and a little bit hungry.

When they were all sitting around the kitchen table, Fran had an idea. 'Shall we tell the story of how Josh and Jaz were adopted?'

'We all know that story,' said Josh.

'Tell it again,' said Jaz.

9

Fran began. 'When you were born, you were very tiny and you had to stay in hospital in a special cot called an incubator, until you were strong enough to go home.

'Your birth mum and dad tried to learn how to take care of you but they couldn't manage because they took bad drugs that made them sick. So you needed a new family of your own.'

Josh said, 'Can we get our life story books with the photos?'

Josh and Jaz have books with their stories written in them. Each book has photos of them as babies, and of their birth mum and dad. They often look at the books with Sue or Fran. Sometimes they add new bits to the story or stick in new photos.

The children went to find the books. When they came back, they all looked at the photos together.

Sue pointed to a picture. 'Josh has his birth mum's curly hair and Jaz has her birth dad's dark eyes.'

'Josh is skinny like Sue,' said Jaz.

'And we take after Fran because we're good at making up games,' said Josh.

Everyone had eaten their egg on toast with crispy bacon.

'Families come in all shapes and sizes,' Sue said.

'Some children live with a mother and a father.

Some children live with a mother or a father.

Some children have stepfathers or stepmothers.

Some live with their grandparents or aunts or uncles.

Some have lots of sisters and brothers, some have only one or two, and some have none.'

'And some children live with two dads or two mums like you,' said Fran.

'And some children are adopted like us,' said Josh and Jaz together.

'But no one else in our class lives with two mums,' said Jaz, 'and I've still got a tummy ache.'

'I still don't want to go to school tomorrow,' groaned Josh.

'As a matter of fact,' said Sue, 'You have got three mums and a dad as well.'

'But that's even worse. I don't want to have one dad and three mums,' said Josh, 'we can't put three mums on our family tree!'

'Do we have to put our birth mum on our family tree?' asked Jaz.

'How about we just pretend we've got one mum and one dad like everybody else?' said Josh.

'Because the other children will laugh at us if we have three mums,' said Jaz.

'Every family tree tells a different story,' explained Fran.

'It would be boring if they were all the same,' added Sue.

'I don't think anyone will laugh if you tell your story well,' said Fran. 'Let's get a big sheet of paper and practise.'

It took Josh and Jaz a long time to draw their family tree.

Mummy Sue and Mummy Fran helped them to make a thick trunk and to draw leaves on the branches for all the people in the family.

They nearly forgot their baby cousin, Billy, because he had only just been born. But they didn't forget Bumps.

Josh drew faces for everyone. Jaz wrote the names underneath each face.

Sue and Fran helped with the spelling because some people had long names like Uncle Jeremy and Granny Heginbotham.

Jaz and Josh
our family Tree

The twins put themselves and their two mums on the longest, strongest branch on the right side of the tree, with all their relatives around them.

They put their birth mum and birth dad and all the relatives they knew about on the left side of the tree.

Josh and Jaz were pleased with their interesting story. Now Jaz didn't have a tummy ache any more, and Josh couldn't wait to go to school tomorrow to show Mr Shah their family tree.

'Hurry up, or we'll be late.'

It was Mummy Fran's turn to take the twins to school next morning.

Jaz and Josh were carrying their rolled up family tree. Fran took Josh and Jaz into their classroom.

'The twins were worried about making their family tree because they don't want to be different,' she told the teacher.

She said they practised making one at home and had brought it to show. Mr Shah was very pleased.

After playtime, Mr Shah said: 'We are going to work on our family trees now. Before we start, Josh and Jaz have something to show us.'

The teacher spread out the twins' family tree on the floor in the reading corner. All the children crowded round. They said 'ooh' and 'wow' and 'cool' and 'brilliant'. No one said anything about having three mums, and nobody laughed.

The teacher said, 'As Josh and Jaz have already made such a beautiful tree, they can help the rest of you to make yours. And don't forget that your own story will be different from everybody else's.'

The children worked hard at their family trees for the rest of the morning.
They asked Josh and Jaz to help them.

One boy didn't know anything about his dad, so Josh helped him to draw a leaf
with a question mark and write 'Dad' underneath. One girl asked Jaz to help her
to sort out her brothers and sisters because some were half-brothers and some
were stepsisters. Another girl wanted to know whether she could put her dead
gran on the family tree.

'Of course you can,' said Josh, 'you can draw a picture of her and write "dead
Gran" underneath.'

When it was dinnertime, all the children put their family trees up on the wall with blue-tack. The twins' tree was the biggest and the teacher put it right in the middle. Josh and Jaz felt very proud.

It was Mummy Fran's turn to collect the twins from school. Josh and Jaz rushed at her and hugged her and dragged her into the classroom to look at the family trees.

As soon as they got home they wanted some tea because they were starving. Then they wanted Mummy Fran to play "Hunt the Giant" and "Race to the Moon" with them.

When Sue got back, they both told her all about the day and how they helped the class to make their family trees.

'Ours was the biggest,' boasted Josh.

'No one laughed,' said Jaz.

'They really were all different,' they both said together.

That evening, Jaz had a tummy ache again and Josh said he didn't feel well enough to go to school tomorrow. They both looked hot and there were spots on their faces.

'Oh dear,' said Sue, 'it looks as though they're coming down with chickenpox after all!'

But Fran said, 'Never mind. I know a lovely game called "Count the Chickenspots"!'